Name: .... Cla

CGP

KS2 English
Comprehension

Year 5

Targeted Question Book

New!

Book Two

KS2 English
Comprehension
Targeted Question Book — Year 5
Book Two

This fantastic Targeted Question Book from CGP is perfect for helping pupils develop their comprehension skills — and broaden their vocabularies.

It contains fifteen texts covering a wide range of authors and genres, including fiction, non-fiction and poetry. Each text is accompanied by a range of comprehension questions that cover all the skills pupils will need for the new National Curriculum.

For even more practice at the same difficulty level, Book One is also available.

Acknowledgements:
p.4: *The Unluckiest Boy in the World* by Andrew Norris (Puffin, 2006) Copyright © Andrew Norris, 2006. Reproduced by permission of Penguin Books Ltd.
Reproduced by permission of The Agency (London) Ltd © Andrew Norris, 2006. First published by Puffin.
p.6: Reproduced by permission of RSPB © 2016 All Rights Reserved. Source: http://www.rspb.org.uk
p.8: From *Johnny and the Dead* by Terry Pratchett adapted by Stephen Briggs (OUP, 2003), copyright © Stephen Briggs 1996, reprinted by permission of the publishers, Oxford University Press
p.10: *Goodnight Mister Tom* by Michelle Magorian (Puffin, 2010). Copyright © Michelle Magorian, 1981. Reproduced by permission of Penguin Books Ltd.
Copyright © 1982 by Michelle Magorian. Used by permission of HarperCollins Publishers.
p.12: © National Geographic Creative
p.14: *I Love the Look of Words* by Maya Angelou, copyright © 1993 by Maya Angelou, from SOUL LOOKS BACK IN WONDER edited by Tom Feelings. Used by permission of Dial Boc Young Readers, an imprint of Penguin Young Readers Group, a division of Penguin Random house LLC.
p.14: *Spellbound* by Adisa.
p.20: Copyright © Highlights for Children, Inc., Columbus, Ohio. All rights reserved. Reprinted by permission.
p.22: Extract from *Candara's Gift* reprinted with permission from Jasper Cooper.
p.26: Abridged extract from an article by Mimi Bekhechi, published in The Independent, 31st May 2016.
p.28: The Society of Authors as the Literary Representative of the Estate of Alfred Noyes.
p.30: © Karen Blumenthal, 16 Feb 2012, *Steve Jobs: The Man Who Thought Different*, Bloomsbury Publishing Plc.

Published by CGP

Editors: Catherine Heygate, Louise McEvoy, Holly Robinson
Consultant: Maxine Petrie

With thanks to Samantha Bensted and Glenn Rogers for the proofreading.
With thanks to Ana Pungartnik for the copyright research.

ISBN: 978 1 78294 701 1

Printed by Elanders Ltd, Newcastle upon Tyne.
Cover image and illustrations on pages 1, 4, 10, 14, 16, 22, 28 and 32 © clipart.com
Image on page 20 © iStock.com.

Text, design, layout and original illustrations
© Coordination Group Publications Ltd. (CGP) 2016

Photocopying this book is not permitted. Extra copies are available from CGP.
0800 1712 712 • www.cgpbooks.co.uk

Contents

Gertrude Ederle

Gertrude Ederle was a famous American swimmer. She set many world records and won three Olympic medals. Her first attempt to swim the English Channel in 1925 failed, but in 1926 she tried again. This time she succeeded, becoming the first woman to swim across the Channel.

The American Swimmer who Waved Away Doubts about Female Athletes

At 7am on 6th August 1926, a 20-year-old American woman stood on the shore of Cap Gris-Nez in France. She was wearing nothing but a bathing suit, motorcycle goggles and a generous slathering of lard*. In front of her, the steely English Channel rolled out towards the horizon.

5　The woman's name was Gertrude Ederle, and she was about to make history. Ederle became the first woman to successfully swim across the English Channel. The gruelling 35-mile journey took her just 14 hours and 39 minutes — almost two hours faster than the existing record, which was set by an Italian man, Enrico Tiraboschi, in 1923.

Ederle's achievement is even more impressive given the stormy weather she encountered along the
10　way. By the end of her swim, she had swum an extra 14 miles as a result of strong winds that blew her off course. The waves became so large that even some ferry crossings were suspended. Ederle was advised to abort her attempt, but she ignored the warnings and carried on.

Around 21:40, Ederle stepped onto a beach around six miles from Dover. Crowds flocked to greet her, cheering and screaming, as she walked unaided onto the shore.

15　**"People said women couldn't swim the Channel. I proved they could."**

The crossing was an amazing feat of athleticism, which challenged widely-held beliefs about women's physical abilities. Only five people had managed to swim across the Channel before her, and all of them were men. Before Ederle's successful swim, many people believed that women weren't physically capable of swimming across the Channel, despite several previous close attempts. In fact, days before
20　Ederle's record was set, another American woman called Clarabelle Barrett had battled the Channel crossing for a whopping 21 hours and 45 minutes before abandoning her swim. In 1924, Danish swimmer Clemington Carson had come within just two miles of land before having to give up.

Ederle's success proved that women weren't just capable of completing the swim — at that time, they could be better at it. Her record remained unbroken until 1950. At a time when women were
25　often considered to be less suited to sports than men, Ederle's achievement forced people to reassess their attitudes towards female athletes. Today, thousands of swimmers (both male and female) have followed in her footsteps.

Written by Louise McEvoy.

Glossary

lard — a solid fat used for cooking

1 Why do you think the author uses the phrase "Waved Away" in the title (line 1)?

....
....

2 marks

2 The author describes the English Channel as "steely" (line 4).
What impression does this description give of the sea?

....
....

1 mark

3 Why do you think the author has made line 15 stand out from the rest of the text?

....
....

2 marks

4 What do you think the word "feat" (line 16) means?

....

1 mark

5 Explain how Gertrude's achievement affected people's attitudes towards women.

....
....

2 marks

6 Explain what this extract tells you about Gertrude's personality.

....

2 marks

....

Total
out of 10

....

The Unluckiest Boy in the World

The Unluckiest Boy in the World tells the story of Nicholas, a boy who becomes cursed after disturbing an old grave. The curse causes disaster to follow Nicholas wherever he goes, so, in this extract, Nicholas' school takes steps to keep him and his fellow pupils safe from the curse.

After that day with Miss Murajee, things did seem to get better, and the number of accidents happening around Nicholas was reduced dramatically.

Mr Fender had panic buttons installed in all the classrooms, connected to the school office. He sent four of his staff on training courses in first aid, and he altered the
5   timetable, as Miss Murajee had suggested, so that Nicholas only had lessons with the more relaxed and easy-going members of staff. Mr Daimon was still away after the mountain-lion incident and Nicholas did science with Mrs Mackintyre, a large, middle-aged woman who never seemed to get upset about anything. His French teacher was replaced by the elderly Mr Dobson, and Mr Fender himself took over the lessons in RE.

10   Some children were moved out of his class. Two of the noisier and more excitable girls were replaced, for instance, by boys from another form whose hobby was collecting wild flowers, and the effect of these changes was soon apparent. Miss Murajee had said that the energy of the curse depended on the emotions of the people around Nicholas and, when the people around him were, by and large, calm and relaxed, the energy for real
15   disaster was no longer there.

Some accidents still happened. There was an incident with a tarantula in a geography lesson that sparked a certain amount of hasty movement, and the number of light bulbs that failed or computers that crashed when Nicholas was around could still reach highly inconvenient levels but, when they did, he knew what to do. As soon as the
20   accident rate threatened to get out of control or to produce an atmosphere of fear and distrust that the curse could feed on, Nicholas would quietly leave the class and head for the Safe Room. [...]

Nicholas noticed the difference as soon as he stepped through the door. That sense he had carried for the last eighteen months of malevolent forces swirling around
25   him, waiting to pounce, disappeared in an instant. It was as if they could no longer see him. He was hidden from their view and, while he was hidden, both he and the people around him were safe.

An abridged extract from *The Unluckiest Boy in the World*
by Andrew Norriss.

1 What do you think might have happened at Nicholas' school before this extract?

....

....

1 mark

2 What does the phrase "by and large" (line 14) mean?

....

1 mark

3 Fill the gap in the sentence below.

This extract is written in the .... person.

1 mark

4 What does the word "malevolent" (line 24) mean? Check your answer in a dictionary.

....

1 mark

5 The school has made several changes because of the curse. Do you think they have done enough to keep pupils and staff safe? Explain your answer.

....

....

2 marks

6 How do you think Nicholas might feel about the effect his curse has on the people around him? Explain your answer.

....

....

2 marks

7 Having read this extract, do you agree that Nicholas is "the unluckiest boy in the world"? Explain your answer.

....

2 marks

....

Total
out of 10

....

Baby Birds

The Royal Society for the Protection of Birds (RSPB) was formed in 1889. It is the biggest conservation charity in Britain. It protects birds and other wildlife in the UK and around the world. This extract from the RSPB's website is all about the challenges that face baby birds.

Cute, fluffy — and hard as nails!

Baby birds are undeniably cute. With their unkempt, fluffy feathers and insistent, squeaky begging calls, they look very appealing to human eyes as well as to those of their parents.

Though things might look idyllic when you see young birds in your garden being fed by attentive adults,
5   life is far from easy for birds.

If an egg is incubated* to the hatching stage — having avoided being eaten, chilled or damaged — the chick's first task is to break free of the shell. Inside the egg, the young bird develops an 'egg tooth' — a hard tip to the upper part of its beak which helps it emerge — but despite that, hatching is physically exhausting.

10   Birds have evolved different strategies to maximise the survival of their offspring. While songbirds emerge from their eggs in a blind, naked state, and are quite unable to do anything for themselves for several weeks, other species — primarily ducks, waders and gamebirds — are ready to go from hatching.

These ground-dwelling birds need to be able to fend and feed for themselves. Though their parents care for them, all hatch with a covering of down* which keeps them warm and camouflages them among
15   the vegetation where they feed. It's crucial, as newly-hatched chicks are popular prey items for many predators, and time is of the essence — pheasant chicks are able to fly after only 12 days!

I'm a fledgling* — get me out of here

Leaving the nest is a hazardous time for all young birds. As well as learning to fly, birds must also learn how to feed and develop predator awareness — the price for not learning quickly enough is high. [...]

20   ### Baby birds in your garden?

It can be tempting to try to 'rescue' a baby bird apparently in trouble.
Here are some things to remember:

- The adult birds are much more skilled at looking after their offspring than humans will ever be!

- It's very likely that the bird's parents are nearby, waiting for you to leave the area. [...]

25   - Try to avoid interference wherever possible. It really is best to leave baby birds alone.

An abridged extract from *www.rspb.org.uk*

Glossary
to incubate (as a bird) — to sit on eggs to keep them warm until they're ready to hatch
down — small, soft feathers   fledgling — a baby bird that's ready to leave its nest

1 "Cute, fluffy — and hard as nails!" (line 1). What does this line tell you about baby birds?

....

1 mark

2 "fluffy feathers" (line 2). This is an example of (circle one):

a. onomatopoeia   b. a metaphor   c. personification   d. alliteration

1 mark

3 Why are songbirds very vulnerable when they first hatch? Explain your answer.

....

....

2 marks

4 What word could the author have used instead of "hazardous" in line 18?

....

1 mark

5 Why are lines 17 and 20 written in bold?

....

1 mark

6 What is the "price" (line 19) of baby birds not developing quickly enough?

....

1 mark

7 Why do you think the author chose to use bullet points in lines 23-25?

....

....

1 mark

8 Why do you think the RSPB published this article? Explain your answer.

....

2 marks

....

Total
out of 10

....

Johnny and the Dead

Johnny and the Dead is a novel by **Terry Pratchett**, which was turned into a play by **Stephen Briggs**. It tells the story of a 12-year-old boy called Johnny Maxwell, who is amazed to discover that he can see and talk to dead people. This extract is from the opening scene of the play.

The cemetery. JOHNNY walks onto the stage, carrying his schoolbag.
He sits on a tombstone and addresses the audience.

JOHNNY: I really discovered the cemetery after I started living at Grandad's, after my parents split up. I started
5 taking a shortcut through here instead of going home on the bus. My pal Wobbler thinks it's
spooky...

WOBBLER enters, carrying a schoolbag.

WOBBLER: Why do we have to go home this way? I think it's spooky.

JOHNNY: *[Still talking to the audience]* But I think it's quite ... friendly. Peaceful. Once you forget about all
the skeletons underground, of course.

10 *WOBBLER sits next to JOHNNY. [...]*

WOBBLER: I bet. I bet ... I bet you wouldn't dare knock on one of those doors. You know, one of them doors on
those big gravestones. I bet something really horrible would come lurchin' out!

WOBBLER stands and lurches about a bit, arms stretched out in front of him.
Then another new thought occurs to him.

15 WOBBLER: 'Ere, my dad says all this is going to be built on. He says the council sold it to some big company
for five pence, cos it was costing too much to keep it going. It's going to be offices and things.

JOHNNY: I'd have given them a pound just to leave it as it is. I bet the people here wouldn't be very happy
about it. If they knew.

JOHNNY points at ALDERMAN BOWLER'S tomb, which has an impressive door,
20 *over which is carved 'Pro Bono Publico'.*

JOHNNY: I bet he'd be really angry.

He crosses to the door and knocks.

WOBBLER: *[Looking worried]* Hey! You mustn't do that!

JOHNNY knocks again. The door opens and ALDERMAN THOMAS BOWLER steps out.
25 *Although his face is a bit on the pale side, he looks comparatively normal, and is dressed in his civic robes.*

A BOWLER: Yes?

JOHNNY cries out in surprise and takes a couple of steps back, bumping into WOBBLER.

WOBBLER: *[startled]* What?

JOHNNY: The door's opened! Can't you see it?

30 WOBBLER: No! No I can't! There's no point in your trying to frighten me, you know. Er ... look, anyway,
I'm late. Um. Bye!

WOBBLER starts to walk off, but quickly breaks into a run.

An abridged extract from *Johnny and the Dead*
by Terry Pratchett, adapted by Stephen Briggs

1 Why are lines 1-2 important for understanding the script?

....

....

1 mark

2 Why do you think the characters' names are written in capital letters?

....

....

1 mark

3 Why do you think the playwright chose to repeat the phrase "I bet" on line 11?

....

1 mark

4 What do you think Wobbler is doing when he "lurches about a bit, arms stretched out in front of him" (line 13)?

....

1 mark

5 How do you think Wobbler feels in lines 30-32? How can you tell?

....

....

2 marks

6 Johnny speaks directly to both the audience and the characters on stage. Why do you think the playwright chose to do this?

....

....

2 marks

7 What book would you like to be turned into a play? Explain your answer.

....

....

2 marks

Total
out of 10

Goodnight Mister Tom

During the Second World War, people were worried about British cities being bombed. Thousands of children were evacuated from cities to the safety of the countryside. *Goodnight Mister Tom* tells the story of an evacuee who is taken in by an old man called Tom Oakley.

"Yes," said Tom bluntly, on opening the front door. "What d'you want?"

A harassed middle-aged woman in a green coat and felt hat stood on his step. He glanced at the armband on her sleeve. She gave him an awkward smile.

"I'm the Billeting Officer* for this area," she began.

5 "Oh yes, and what's that go to do wi' me?"

She flushed slightly. "Well, Mr, Mr…"

"Oakley. Thomas Oakley."

"Ah, thank you, Mr Oakley." She paused and took a deep breath. "Mr Oakley, with the declaration of war imminent…"

10 Tom waved his hand. "I knows all that. Git to the point. What d'you want?" He noticed a small boy at her side.

"It's him I've come about," she said. "I'm on my way to your village hall with the others."

"What others?"

She stepped to one side. Behind the large iron gate which stood at the end of the
15 graveyard were a small group of children. Many of them were filthy and very poorly clad*. Only a handful had a blazer or coat. They all looked bewildered and exhausted. One tiny dark-haired girl in the front was hanging firmly on to a new teddy-bear.

The woman touched the boy at her side and pushed him forward.

"There's no need to tell me," said Tom. "It's obligatory and it's for the war effort."

20 "You are entitled to choose your child, I know," began the woman apologetically.

Tom gave a snort.

"But," she continued, "his mother wants him to be with someone who's religious or near a church. She was quite adamant*. Said she would only let him be evacuated if he was."

"Was what?" asked Tom impatiently.

25 "Near a church."

Tom took a second look at the child. The boy was thin and sickly-looking, pale with limp sandy hair and dull grey eyes.

Glossary

Billeting Officer — the person in charge of finding homes for evacuees

clad — dressed   **adamant** — unwilling to compromise

An extract from
Goodnight Mister Tom
by Michelle Magorian.

1 Why doesn't the author use Standard English for Tom's speech?

....

....

1 mark

2 How do you think the Billeting Officer feels when she is talking to Tom? Explain your answer.

....

....

2 marks

3 Write down a word that the author could have used instead of "bewildered" in line 16.

....

1 mark

4 What effect does line 17 have on the reader? Explain your answer.

....

....

2 marks

5 Does Tom have to take in an evacuee? Explain your answer.

....

1 mark

6 Give one reason why the author might have chosen to include a lot of direct speech in this text.

....

1 mark

7 Do you think that Tom and the boy will get on? Explain your answer.

....

2 marks

....

Total
out of 10

....

Facts about Hurricanes!

Hurricanes are huge tropical storms which form far out at sea. Sometimes they reach land, where they can do lots of damage. Hurricanes are very common in some parts of the world, but fortunately they don't often affect the UK. This text is full of interesting facts about hurricanes.

Hold on tight, gang — and we mean super tight! — because we're about to check out ten facts on one of nature's most powerful forces — hurricanes!

- Hurricanes are giant tropical storms that produce heavy rainfall and *super*-strong winds.

5
- Hurricanes form over warm ocean waters near the equator. The warm, moist air above the ocean surface rises, causing air from surrounding areas to be 'sucked' in. This 'new' air then becomes warm and moist, and rises, too, beginning a continuous cycle that forms clouds. The clouds then rotate with the spin of the Earth. If there is enough warm water to feed the storm, a hurricane forms!

10
- Hurricanes rotate around a circular centre called the 'eye', where it is generally calm with no clouds. Surrounding the eye is the eye wall — the most dangerous part of the hurricane with the strongest winds, thickest clouds and heaviest rain!

- Most hurricanes occur harmlessly out at sea. However, when they move towards land they can be incredibly dangerous and cause serious damage.

15
- The strong spiralling winds of a hurricane can reach speeds of up to 320 kmph — strong enough to rip up entire trees and destroy buildings!

- In the southern hemisphere, hurricanes rotate in a clockwise direction, and in the northern hemisphere they rotate in an anticlockwise direction. This is due to what's called the Coriolis Force, produced by the Earth's rotation.

20
- When a hurricane reaches land it often produces a 'storm surge'. This is when the high winds drive the sea toward the shore, causing water levels to rise and creating large crashing waves. Storm surges can reach 6 m high and extend to over 150 km!

- Hurricanes are also called cyclones and typhoons, depending on where they occur. In the Atlantic Ocean and northeast Pacific they are hurricanes, in the northwest Pacific they are typhoons and in the South Pacific and Indian Ocean they are cyclones.

25
- The largest hurricane on record is Typhoon Tip, which occurred in 1979 in the northwest Pacific. With a diameter of around 2,220 km, it was nearly half the size of the United States!

- Hurricanes are given names by the World Meteorological Organisation (WMO) so that they can be distinguished. Each year, tropical storms are named in alphabetical order
30 according to a list produced by the WMO. That name stays with the storm if it develops into a hurricane. The names can only be repeated after six years.

An article from *www.ngkids.co.uk*

1 Why is the word "super" written in italics in line 3?

....

....

1 mark

2 Why don't hurricanes form over cold oceans?

....

1 mark

3 Who do you think this text is aimed at? How can you tell?

....

....

2 marks

4 Why do you think the author uses a lot of exclamation marks in this text?

....

....

1 mark

5 The author compares the size of Typhoon Tip to the size of the United States (lines 26-27). Why do you think they did this?

....

....

2 marks

6 The purpose of this text is (circle one):

a. to persuade and inform   b. to inform and entertain   c. to entertain and persuade

1 mark

7 Why do you think hurricanes are more dangerous on land than they are out at sea?

....

....

2 marks

Total
out of 10

Poems about Words

Adisa is a performance poet who aims to get as many people as possible interested in poetry. Maya Angelou was a famous American poet and writer. She was well known for the powerful way she performed her poems. Both these poems explore the pleasure of language and words.

Spellbound (abridged)

Ride with me
On this lyrical roller coaster
My syllable slices
Will feed your hunger
5   As they pop up and down
Like a Jamaican toaster

[...]

Submerge yourself, in this
Lip-hop metaphor
Resistance is futile,
10   As I hold the key to the door

I leave you tongue-tied like Houdini
You'll never escape my barrel of words
Your belly expands with laughter
As you guzzle on my contagious verbs

15   My acid adjectives
Hack deep into your heart
Reprogramming your software
Be afraid!
Be very afraid
20   For this is just the start

Adisa

I Love the Look of Words (an extract)

Popcorn leaps, popping from the floor
of a hot black skillet*
and into my mouth.
Black words leap,
5   snapping from the white
page. Rushing into my eyes. Sliding
into my brain which gobbles them
the way my tongue and teeth
chomp the buttered popcorn.

10   When I have stopped reading,
ideas from the words stay stuck
in my mind, like the sweet
smell of butter perfuming my
fingers long after the popcorn
15   is finished.

Maya Angelou

Glossary
skillet — frying pan

1 Find and copy one simile from lines 1-6 of *Spellbound*.

....

1 mark

2 *Spellbound* uses the pronoun "you". What effect does this have on the reader?

....

....

1 mark

3 a. What is the message of lines 10-15 of *I Love the Look of Words*?

....

....

2 marks

b. How similar is the message of lines 15-18 of *Spellbound*? Explain your answer.

....

....

2 marks

4 Both poems compare words to food. Why do you think the poets chose this comparison?

....

....

....

2 marks

5 Which poem do you prefer? Explain your answer.

....

2 marks

....

Total
out of 10

....

The Oak and the Linden Tree

The people of Ancient Rome believed in lots of different gods and goddesses and told many stories about them. This extract is based on a myth by Ovid, a famous poet who lived in Ancient Rome around 2000 years ago. It focuses on Jupiter, king of the gods, and his son, Mercury.

Many centuries ago, in the far distant past, Mount Olympus was the home of the gods. On this great mountain, there was no place for sadness, hunger or thirst. The gods had all they needed, and more. The most delicious feasts satisfied their bodies, while beautiful music fed their souls. And every day, the goddesses would entertain them all with stories of old.

5 But Jupiter, king of the gods, had grown restless. In this perfect place, there was nothing to do. He decided it was time to descend from Olympus and visit the people of Earth below.

"Mercury," he boomed. "Mercury, my son! We have an important task to perform."

Mercury appeared at his father's side, and his eager eyes searched the wise, old face. Mercury had great respect for his father, and always valued opportunities to please and impress him.

10 "Where are we going, Father? What shall we do?"

"It's time we tested the kindness of those on Earth. We shall visit the people of Phrygia [pronounced FRI-gee-a]. If they pass the test, then all shall be well. If they fail the test, then they'll learn the hard way that unkind behaviour provokes the anger of the gods."

Mercury nodded and rose at once. He removed his magical winged sandals which let him fly as 15 fast as the wind, and both gods put on old tattered clothes. Jupiter set off with a slow, painful limp, and Mercury, barefooted, followed behind.

Mercury and Jupiter arrived in Phrygia looking like two humble travellers. They started their task, knocking wearily on each door that they found.

"Could you spare us a drink of water, please?" asked Mercury.

20 "We have no food and nowhere to go," cried Jupiter.

But the people of Phrygia slammed their doors in the gods' faces and paid no attention to their pleas for help. At last, Mercury and Jupiter turned in despair to a lonely shack, which cowered and bowed its straw head. It was the smallest house they'd seen so far, and the walls quivered in the gentle breeze. 25 Drawing near, they saw a couple inside. The man, Philemon [fi-lee-mon], and his wife, Baucis [baw-sis], turned their heads at the sound of the knock. Philemon hurried over to answer the door.

30 "Please, would you let us sit for a while? We are tired and hungry, and have travelled far."

Philemon's face broke into a welcoming smile, and he beamed at the visitors. "Why, of course, strangers! Please, enter our home!"

Based on a myth by Ovid.

1 Are you surprised that Jupiter wanted to leave Mount Olympus? Explain your answer.

....

....
2 marks

2 Why do you think Mercury left his sandals behind when he and Jupiter went to Earth?

....
1 mark

3 Summarise what happens in lines 17-22.

....

....
2 marks

4 "bowed its straw head" (line 24). This is an example of (circle one):

a. onomatopoeia   b. a simile   c. personification   d. alliteration
1 mark

5 Write down two features of this text that show it's a myth.

....

....
2 marks

6 What do you think will happen in the rest of the myth?

....
2 marks

....

....

Total
out of 10

Cora and the King

Cora and the King is a story about a young girl called Cora whose village is left starving after a drought. After her attempts to beg the King for food fail, Cora joins a plot to overthrow him. When the plot is uncovered, Cora is arrested and taken to the castle to await her trial.

Cora and her captor eventually arrive at the castle. As she stands before the towering stone walls, her throat feels dry and her hands are trembling so much her shackles begin to clatter. She raises her eyes to the sky and inhales deeply. Greedily, she drinks in the rays of the weak afternoon sun which illuminate her pale skin.

5 "You're right to make the most of it," says a cold, gleeful voice. The castle porter*, in the process of opening the great wooden door, pauses to eye her curiously. "You won't be able to enjoy it much longer. The charges against you are stacked about as high as this tower."

Cora remains exactly where she is, and with a quavering voice says, "Even the tallest towers can come tumbling down."

10 The porter scowls at her for a moment before shaking his head. He heaves open the heavy door and leads Cora to a small dingy cell at the base of the castle's tallest tower. As the lock scrapes and the porter's thudding footsteps recede, an oppressive, tomb-like silence slinks into the room. It wraps itself around Cora and seems to press her from all sides.

Cora peers around in the gloom, then stares in astonishment. A thin shaft of light is floating
15 uncertainly in the darkness. She drops to her knees and crawls towards its source. It seems to be coming from under the bed. She wriggles beneath the frame, then jumps as a large spider scuttles out in panic. Undeterred, Cora drags herself further forward and feels along the rugged stone wall. A small wooden hatch! It's bolted from the outside, but a tiny gap is visible where one of the panels has begun to rot. Cora's eyes shine in the darkness. She digs her
20 nails into the softened wood and patiently begins to scrape.

***

A rabbit lollops along the grass in front of the castle. The first rays of the sun are peeping above the high tower, and a warm pink glow yawns and stretches itself across the cold blue landscape. The rabbit pauses. It watches with interest as a creature emerges from a burrow by the tower. First comes a head with long dark hair, then comes a stocky body. The rabbit
25 waggles its ears and narrows its eyes as the creature twists and squirms and eventually collapses onto the grass. Straightening up, the creature begins to creep around the edge of the castle. The rabbit looks on, puzzled for a moment, then bobs away into the lightening dawn.

Written by Louise McEvoy.

<u>Glossary</u>

castle porter — person responsible for letting people in and out of a castle

1 How do you think Cora is feeling in lines 1-4? Explain your answer.

....

....

2 marks

2 What do you think Cora means when she says
"Even the tallest towers can come tumbling down" (lines 8-9)?

....

....

1 mark

3 This extract is written in the present tense. What effect does this have on the reader?

....

....

2 marks

4 The phrase "the porter's thudding footsteps" on line 12 is an example of (circle one):

a. alliteration   b. personification   c. onomatopoeia   d. a metaphor

1 mark

5 The author writes from a different perspective in lines 21-27.
Explain how this helps to create tension in the extract.

....

....

2 marks

6 Would you like Cora to succeed in her escape from the castle? Explain your answer.

....

2 marks

....

Total
out of 10

....

Robot on the Ice

Meteorites are rocks that have fallen to Earth from outer space. Scientists study meteorites because they provide lots of information about what space is like. This article explains how a team of scientists from the USA built a special robot that could find meteorites in Antarctica.

A Wandering Robot

We called our robot Nomad. We had designed it to explore remote places, just as a space robot explores other planets. Nomad had to be able to travel over
5 rough ground and drive for long distances. It had to be able to look around, study objects that we had programmed it to look for, and send its information back to humans. So we gave Nomad a sturdy frame, four wheels, lots of sensors and computers, and wireless
10 access so that humans could communicate with it.

Nomad had already explored a desert in South America, but before we went to Antarctica we had to make some changes. We added heaters to keep the computers and sensors warm, and we added studs to the tyres so Nomad could move on the ice without slipping. [...]

The spectrometer* was attached to the end of Nomad's robot arm, so Nomad could lower the
15 sensor onto rocks. The spectrometer measures changes in light as the light reflects off rock. Using those changes, Nomad can tell better than our eyes if a rock is a meteorite or an ordinary rock. We call those ordinary rocks "meteor-wrongs".

Dr. William "Red" Whittaker, director of the Field Robotics Center, said that Nomad was a new kind of robot because it could search on its own and even sort meteorites from Earth rocks. [...]

20 ## Searching for Meteorites

We started up the robot and all its computers, and told it to start searching. But Antarctica is very different from Pennsylvania, where we had done most of our original testing. We needed to test Nomad in this new environment, and we had to make some changes to the software and the sensors.

25 Finally, we had everything working, and we sent off the robot. We sat in our tent and watched Nomad's progress from our computers. It found several ordinary rocks, and then, suddenly, my computer screen flashed an alert. Nomad had found a meteorite!

Nomad found several more meteorites before we left Antarctica. After we returned to the United States, scientists began to study the rocks for clues about outer space. And our robot
30 had returned a hero.

Glossary
spectrometer — a kind of sensor

An abridged article, written by Kimberly Shillcutt Tyree, PhD.

1 Why did the team need to make alterations to Nomad before taking it to Antarctica?

....

....

1 mark

2 Why do you think the team call ordinary rocks "meteor-wrongs" (line 17)?

....

....

1 mark

3 How do you think the author felt when Nomad found its first meteorite in Antarctica? How can you tell?

....

....

2 marks

4 Do you find the layout of this text helpful? Explain your answer.

....

....

2 marks

5 Look up the word "nomad" in a dictionary.
Why do you think the team chose to call their robot "Nomad"?

....

....

2 marks

6 The author describes Nomad as a "hero" (line 30). Do you agree that it is a hero?

....

2 marks

....

....

Total
out of 10

Candara's Gift

Candara's Gift is the first book in a fantasy trilogy set in the magical Kingdom of Gems. The Kingdom has enjoyed more than 500 years of peace and happiness, but all this comes to an end when a menacing figure slips into the Kingdom under the cover of darkness...

The tall figure approached the woods with powerful strides. Just behind him, held on a metal chain which he shook every so often to keep it moving, was a great creature. As the darkly cloaked man and the creature moved, the plants nearby withered, their leaves falling to the dying grass, and flowers, so bright and beautiful the day before, drooped as
5   if touched by invisible poisonous vapours.

Close by, and high up in an old oak tree, perched a snowy owl called Joog. [...]

Joog was meant to be watching. He was always particularly
vigilant during nighttime as it was his job to guard the
kingdom, but tonight, however, he had slipped into a deep
10   and absorbing slumber leaving the kingdom unprotected
and open to intruders.

The wild wind whistled and sighed through the trees.
It swept across the kingdom from the west, like a
curtain drawn at the end of the day and now it persisted
15   deep into the night, swirling across the whole kingdom with
a groaning presence. It seemed to herald the arrival of
something unusual, bleak and unwelcome, something that forewarned of danger.
In spite of this howling wind, however, Joog slept soundly and so did every creature in
the Kingdom of Gems. Even the nocturnal animals were sleeping which was strange
20   because during the dark hours of the night they were usually busy.

Then, as the dawn approached, the air seemed to grow weary of its swirling movements
and the driving wind collapsed, like an exhausted wild animal that finally runs out of
energy. But this was not a peaceful stilling, it was as if the air grew too heavy to be in
motion any more, too thick to stir and its dreadful weight fell upon the land. The utter
25   stillness that filled the kingdom, seeping into the very earth, was a brooding expectant
atmosphere. The whole kingdom seemed to be wrapped in a weighty darkness, grave
and intense, that awaited the arrival of something uninvited and unwanted.

Joog was still absorbed in a deep sleep.

Then a rustling sound, at first distant in the still air, but soon growing louder, broke the
30   heavy silence. The shadowy figure, with the great creature following, was moving into
the woodlands and striding steadily over the spongy leaf-strewn earth. Joog did not hear
these approaching footsteps. He did not feel the strange sinister chill that had suddenly
filled the air. He did not see the dark-cloaked figure far below him cross the border and
enter the Kingdom. A Troubler had arrived.

An abridged extract from *Candara's Gift* by Jasper Cooper.

1 Write down one feature of this text that shows it is an extract from a fantasy novel.

....

1 mark

2 What do you think the word "vigilant" (line 8) means? Check your answer in a dictionary.

....

1 mark

3 Find and copy one simile from lines 12-20.

....

1 mark

4 Why do you think that every creature in the kingdom "slept soundly" (line 18)?

....

1 mark

5 "the air seemed to grow weary" (line 21). This is an example of (circle one):

a. personification   b. a simile   c. alliteration   d. onomatopoeia

1 mark

6 In lines 21-27, how does the author suggest that something bad is going to happen?

....

....

2 marks

7 The character who has just arrived in the kingdom is called a "Troubler" (line 34).
Why do you think the author chose this name?

....

1 mark

8 How do you think Joog will feel when he wakes up? Give reasons for your answer.

....

2 marks

....

Total
out of 10

....

The Hound of the Baskervilles

Arthur Conan Doyle is best known for creating the fictional detective Sherlock Holmes. *The Hound of the Baskervilles* was his third novel about Holmes. In this extract, Holmes and his companion, Dr Watson, discuss a clue left in their apartment by a mysterious visitor.

"Well, Watson, what do you make of it?"

Holmes was sitting with his back to me, and I had given him no sign of my occupation.

"How did you know what I was doing? I believe you have eyes in the back of your head."

"I have, at least, a well-polished, silver-plated coffee-pot in front of me," said he. "But, tell me,
5   Watson, what do you make of our visitor's stick? Since we have been so unlucky as to miss him and have no knowledge of why he was here, this accidental souvenir becomes of importance. Let me hear you create a profile of the man by examining it."

"I think," said I, following Holmes's methods as far as I could, "that Dr. Mortimer is a successful, elderly medical man, respected since those who know him gave him this stick as a mark of their
10   appreciation."

"Good!" said Holmes. "Excellent!"

"I think also that it is likely that he is a country doctor who does a great deal of his visiting on foot."

"Why so?"

15   "Because this stick, though originally a very handsome one, has been so knocked about that I can hardly imagine a town doctor carrying it. The thick iron base is worn down, so it is evident that he has done a great amount of walking with it."

"Perfectly sound!" said Holmes, "really, Watson, you excel yourself."

He had never said as much before, and I must admit that his words gave me great pleasure. I was
20   proud, too, to think that I had mastered his system so well that I could apply it in a way which earned his approval. He now took the stick from my hands and examined it for a few minutes with his naked eyes.

"Interesting, though elementary*," said he as he returned to his favourite corner of the settee. "There are certainly one or two clues upon the stick. It gives us the basis for several deductions."

25   "Has anything escaped me?" I asked with some self-importance. "I trust that there is nothing of importance which I have overlooked?"

"I am afraid, my dear Watson, that most of your conclusions were wrong, although in noting your mistakes I was occasionally guided towards the truth."

An adapted extract from *The Hound of the Baskervilles* by Arthur Conan Doyle.

> **Glossary**
>
> elementary — easy to understand

1 How did Holmes know that Watson was standing behind him?

....

1 mark

2 What do you think the word "deductions" (line 24) means? Check your answer in a dictionary.

....

1 mark

3 a. How do you think Watson feels in lines 19-21? Why does he feel this way?

....

....

2 marks

b. Do you think Watson's feelings have changed by the end of the extract?
Explain your answer.

....

....

2 marks

4 Is the language in this extract formal or informal? Explain your answer.

....

....

2 marks

5 Write down two adjectives to describe Sherlock Holmes's personality. Explain your choices.

....

2 marks

....

....

Total
out of 10

Harambe the Gorilla

In May 2016, a three-year-old boy climbed into a gorilla enclosure at Cincinnati Zoo in the USA. To protect the child, staff at the zoo shot dead the gorilla who lived in the enclosure — a large male called Harambe. This article argues that it is wrong to keep animals like gorillas in zoos.

The only thing more upsetting than Harambe the gorilla's death was the reality of his life

Surely we can begin to agree that animals which share 98 per cent of our DNA should not be kept as entertainment for us to gawk at in a zoo.

Yet again, captivity has taken an animal's life. The
5 latest victim: a 17-year-old gorilla named Harambe, who was gunned down after a young boy managed to crawl through a fence before falling into his enclosure at the Cincinnati Zoo.

The incident (which could have been prevented
10 by surrounding the enclosure with a secondary barrier) has generated a great deal of debate online. […] What we should be asking is why intelligent, self-aware animals are *still* being displayed as living exhibits for humans to gawk at.

15 Harambe and other animals serving life sentences in zoos are leading lives of quiet desperation. They are denied the most basic freedoms, including being able to choose where to roam, when and what to eat, and whom to socialise with. It's no
20 wonder that these magnificent animals frequently exhibit signs of extreme depression and related psychological conditions. […]

Zoos try to justify their existence in the name of "conservation*", but warehousing animals in these
25 facilities does nothing to help protect endangered animals in the wild. In fact, some say doing so actually harms wild populations because it diverts much-needed funds away from the protection of animals in their natural habitats.

30 After all, capturing (yes, some zoos still snatch animals out of their natural habitats), transporting and maintaining non-human animals for the professed purpose of "conserving" them is enormously expensive. It costs about 50 times
35 as much to keep one African elephant in a zoo as it would to safeguard sufficient natural habitat to sustain that elephant and countless others.

When, in 2007, the Zoological Society of London spent £5.3m on a new gorilla enclosure, Ian
40 Redmond, the chief consultant to the UN Great Apes Survival Partnership, said: "£5m for three gorillas [seems a huge amount] when national parks are seeing [three gorillas] killed every day for want of some Land Rovers, trained men and anti-
45 poaching patrols. It must be very frustrating for the warden of a national park to see". Clearly, the same amount of money a zoo spends on buying expensive animals could benefit so many more of the same animals living in the wild. Our need
50 for entertainment is expensive, unnecessary and without discernible* benefit, then, to the animals involved.

Abridged article from *www.independent.co.uk*

Glossary

(wildlife) conservation — ensuring the survival of wild plants and animals   discernible — noticeable

1 The author says that animals are "serving life sentences in zoos" (lines 15-16). Why do you think she chose this phrase?

....

....

2 marks

2 Tick the correct box in the table below to show whether each statement is a fact or an opinion.

	Fact	Opinion
Animals should not be kept for people to gawk at in zoos.		
The shooting of Harambe led to a lot of debate online.		
Zoo animals lead lives of quiet desperation.		

2 marks

3 In your own words, summarise the information in lines 23-29.

....

....

....

2 marks

4 Do you think the zoo was right to shoot Harambe to protect the young child? Explain your answer.

....

....

....

2 marks

5 Do you think keeping animals in zoos is a good or bad idea? Explain your answer.

....

2 marks

....

Total
out of 10

....

The Highwayman

The *Highwayman* was written by Alfred Noyes in 1906. It is about a highwayman (someone who robbed travellers on the roads) and his doomed relationship with a woman called Bess. This extract, which is taken from the start of the poem, uses dramatic language to set the scene.

The wind was a torrent* of darkness among the gusty trees.
The moon was a ghostly galleon* tossed upon cloudy seas.
The road was a ribbon of moonlight over the purple moor,
And the highwayman came riding—
5   Riding—riding—
The highwayman came riding, up to the old inn-door.

He'd a French cocked-hat* on his forehead, a bunch of lace at his chin,
A coat of the claret* velvet, and breeches of brown doe-skin.
They fitted with never a wrinkle. His boots were up to the thigh.
10 And he rode with a jewelled twinkle,
      His pistol butts a-twinkle,
His rapier hilt* a-twinkle, under the jewelled sky.

Over the cobbles he clattered and clashed in the dark inn-yard.
He tapped with his whip on the shutters, but all was locked and barred.
15 He whistled a tune to the window, and who should be waiting there
But the landlord's black-eyed daughter,
      Bess, the landlord's daughter,
Plaiting a dark red love-knot into her long black hair.

And dark in the dark old inn-yard a stable-wicket* creaked
20 Where Tim the ostler* listened. His face was white and peaked*.
His eyes were hollows of madness, his hair like mouldy hay,
But he loved the landlord's daughter,
      The landlord's red-lipped daughter.
Dumb as a dog he listened, and he heard the robber say —

Alfred Noyes

Glossary

torrent — a fast stream	galleon — a large sailing ship	cocked-hat — a triangular hat
claret — dark red	rapier hilt — the handle of a sword	wicket — gate
ostler — someone who looks after horses		peaked — sickly

1 What is the rhyming pattern of this poem? Circle one.

a. AABBCC   b. ABABAB   c. AABCCB   d. ABCABC

1 mark

2 Find and copy a metaphor from lines 1-6.

....

1 mark

3 "The moon was a ghostly galleon tossed upon cloudy seas" (line 2).
What effect does this line have on the reader?

....

....

2 marks

4 What does the poet mean by "the jewelled sky" (line 12)?

....

1 mark

5 "Over the cobbles he clattered and clashed" (line 13). This is an example of (circle one):

a. a metaphor   b. a simile   c. personification   d. alliteration

1 mark

6 Explain how the poet shows that Tim the ostler is an unpleasant character.

....

....

....

2 marks

7 Does this extract make you want to read the rest of *The Highwayman*? Explain your answer.

....

2 marks

....

Total
out of 10

....

Steve Jobs' Biography

Steve Jobs was an American businessman and inventor. In the 1970s, he co-founded Apple Inc, which has become one of the world's most successful technology companies. This extract from Steve's biography describes his personality and some key events in his life.

In his early twenties, Jobs almost single-handedly introduced the world to the first computer that could sit on your desk and actually do something all by itself. He revolutionized music and the ears of a generation with a spiffy little music player called the iPod and a wide selection of songs at the iTunes store. He funded and nurtured a
5   company called Pixar that made the most amazing computer-animated movies — *Toy Story*, *Cars*, and *Finding Nemo* — bringing to life imaginary characters like never before.

Though he was neither an engineer nor a computer geek, he helped create one gotta-have-it product after another by always designing it with you and me, the actual users, in mind. [...] [M]ore insanely awesome technology was in the works, including
10   the iPhone, which would put much of the power of a computer neatly into the palm of your hand. The father of four would be repeatedly compared with the inventor Thomas Edison and auto magnate* Henry Ford, who both introduced affordable, life-changing conveniences that transformed the way Americans lived.

Yet for all his successes, Jobs also endured some very public failures. When he
15   was thirty years old, he was summarily* stripped of his duties at Apple for being too disruptive and difficult. He set out to build another computer company and missed the mark, blowing through millions of dollars of investors' money. He could be volatile*, screaming at associates, competitors, and reporters. He sometimes cried when things didn't go his way and he regularly took credit for the ideas of others. He could be both
20   charming and gratingly abrasive*, sensitive and stunningly mean-spirited.

Some parts of his life sounded like a fairy tale right out of the movies: there was a promise made when he was a baby, romances, remarkable rebounds*, and riches almost too big to be believed. Other parts were so messy and ugly, so very human, that they would never be considered family entertainment. He was both loved and hated, intensely
25   admired and widely dismissed. People described him with the strongest words: visionary*. Showman. Artist. Tyrant. Genius. Jerk.

An abridged extract from *Steve Jobs: The Man Who Thought Different* by Karen Blumenthal.

Glossary		
magnate — a successful businessman		summarily — suddenly
volatile — unpredictable	abrasive — harsh	rebounds — recoveries
visionary — someone with a clear vision of how the future should be		

1 Give one feature of this extract that shows it is a biography, not an autobiography.

....

1 mark

2 What do you think the word "nurtured" (line 4) means? Check your answer in a dictionary.

....

1 mark

3 Do you think the author likes the products that Steve worked on? Explain your answer.

....

....

2 marks

4 How do you think Steve might have felt when he was "stripped of his duties" (line 15) at Apple? Explain your answer.

....

....

2 marks

5 What do you notice about the punctuation of line 26?
Why do you think the author has punctuated line 26 in this way?

....

....

....

2 marks

6 Do you think you would have wanted to meet Steve? Give reasons for your answer.

....

2 marks

....

Total
out of 10

....

Animal Adventures

By now, you've had plenty of practice at reading texts and answering questions. Now it's time to write your own text, think of some questions, and then swap with a friend.

Write a poem about your favourite animal. Make sure you include plenty of descriptive language, and use techniques like similes, metaphors and alliteration to bring your animal to life.